MY DAILY MOMENTUM

90-Day Journal for a Productive Life
by Allie Pleiter

Copyright

PRINT ISBNs:
9781735727301 (Rose)
9781735727325 (Blue)
9781735727318 (Orange)
9780997298291 (Green)

Graphic Design: Rose Kostan-Schwartz, Creative Design Solutions
'image: Flaticon.com'. This publication has been designed using resources from Flaticon.com

Table of Contents:

Introduction

"How do I get it done?"
"How do I get there from here?"
"Why aren't I where I want to be?"

Life seems to come at us non-stop and full-force. A groaning mountain of tasks pulls at our attention and energy from sun-up until long after sundown. Rare is the day when most of us put our head to the pillow with anything close to peace and satisfaction.

This journal is the best weapon I know against that daily onslaught. It is born from a practice I began when I had to figure out how to get through the chaotic and devastating days of my son facing several life-threatening illnesses (he is healthy and well now). What I discovered not only helped me through those crises, but every day. Every single day for over ten years and counting.

I can say without a doubt that this daily and monthly practice has been the momentum behind my business success, my personal growth, my spiritual growth, and my general happiness.

I use the word momentum deliberately. Momentum creates movement and progress. Momentum is the step today that prepares you for tomorrow. Momentum propels you forward when forces work against you. Momentum fosters persistence, vision, patience, and even the willingness to do it all over again one more day.

Most of all, momentum is completely within your power. It is something you create. A choice you make, right now, today.

I believe momentum is the secret. Talent is lovely, luck (if you believe in it) is fickle, opportunities come and go, business markets aren't in our control, but your momentum is always up to you. Every day. It's life's "secret sauce." And you can't keep a secret like that under wraps—it demands to be shared. So I am privileged to share it with you.

My fervent hope and prayer is that this journal does for you what it has done for me: chart a path to a productive, happy, and satisfying life through just about anything the world can throw at you. I'd be honored if you would share how your journey is going with me at allie@alliepleiter.com.

Onward, dear friend. Because I deeply believe "Momentum is how you get there from here."

—*Allie*

How to Use This Journal

The Daily Practice

Momentum is indeed a daily practice. These pages guide you through the daily reflection that creates and nurtures momentum.

Each day in this journal has two facing pages. The left facing page outlines a series of lists while the right facing page is open for your own writing.

Inspirational Reading

Make sure you are filling your mind with good things every day. Whether for you it is scripture, inspirational literature, biographies of your heroes, or any daily reflective texts, make sure you bring a small inspirational passage into your day. Notate what you're reading at the top of the left facing page so you can see what's inspired some of the thoughts you have recorded on that day.

Positives

It is crucial to start every reflective time with a focus on the positives. Start by filling in the list on the left facing page with three good things about your life today. Call them blessings, gratitude list, positives—I use an icon so that you can think of them in whatever word works for you. Keep them as immediate as possible, listing things from the day before or good things on the way in the day ahead. This positive-first exercise not only forces you to unearth the good in every single day (admittedly much more challenging on some days than others), but serves as a gentle reminder to your subconscious to keep the radar up for good things to go next on your list.

Some examples:

- The beautiful sunrise and lovely weather predicted for today.
- The phone call from a friend that arrived just when you needed it yesterday.
- Praise from a boss or colleague.
- The element of health or healing you saw yesterday and hope for more of today.

The Day Ahead

Now focus on the day ahead. This second left facing page list is for prayers, or intentions, or goals—again, use the word that speaks to you. These are just for the day ahead. Don't fall into long term issues here. Remember that even life's thorniest problems or greatest accomplishments are tackled one day at a time. Think about what today's needs are and set out your plans to meet them. Of course, there are likely more than three, but here is a place to identify the most important, the most impactful, or at the very least, the ones in your control. If you are a person of faith, then bring that into your list and say prayers for the help you need.

Some examples:

- Having an effective conversation or meeting with a colleague.

- Finding a solution to a household or personal issue.

- Asking someone for help with a challenge you are facing.

- Any specific task that needs to get done in the day ahead.

Avoid

This final left facing page list allows you to plot out three things to avoid. Think of it as a "don't" list rather than a "to-do" list. Every day holds traps to steer clear of and rabbit holes not to go down. We often forget to tell ourselves to avoid such things. Make the declaration of what you won't allow to happen today. Of course you won't always succeed, but setting the intention can have surprising power.

Some examples:

- "Scarcity thinking"—I don't have enough, I'm not strong enough, there's not enough time, etc.

- Worrying about something you have no control over.

- Letting a contentious person goad you into an argument.

- Judging someone when you may not have the full story.

Affirm

Lifting someone else up is powerful energy. Who can you affirm today? Fill in this line with an intention to pay a compliment, thank someone for their hard work, show a bit of encouragement, or just check in with someone going through a hard time. Making this part of your day not only sends good things out into the world, but helps you feel useful, powerful, and grateful—all keys to ongoing momentum

Reflect

Fill the rest of that day's pages with reflections on what you are thinking and feeling. What's on your mind? Where are you seeing new progress or old issues resurfacing? What about the inspirational reading for the day strikes you? I have often joked, "I don't know what I think about something until I write about it." Take some time to explore what is going on in your world and how it is impacting you. If you are a person of faith, feel free to use these lines as the place to write out your prayers. Mull over things that are sticking in your mind and lessons you see heading your way. Not every day will fill up every line. But take the space here to be thoughtful about yourself and your circumstances. Journaling has always been a powerful practice for self-awareness and goal setting. Let that process happen in a daily dose here.

One more thing...every day:

Look back on yesterday's prayers/wishes/goals and check off those that were accomplished. It is amazing how that concrete evidence of things happening can bolster your confidence and faith.

Look back on yesterday's "to avoids" and rate yourself. Did you avoid it, or did it get the best of you? Hold yourself accountable, but do it with kindness.

Did you affirm the person you set out to compliment or encourage? This one can be easy to let slip. Keep track—and note the outcome if it's especially powerful.

Once a month, take these daily reflections and fold them into a Big Thinking Day.

Big Thinking Day

Life rarely affords us the chance to think big. Daily demands crowd out the mental space needed to ponder, reflect, plan, and dream. It's easy to get stuck in the maze, unable to climb up and see a broader picture.

We all know we should take the time for that long-range, high altitude view. Finding that time, however, looms difficult for most of us. How many of us sink exhausted into a chair at the end of a weary day, dreaming of a quiet beach house where deep and valuable thoughts would show up?

And that's the problem right there. Most of us don't have access to a beach retreat, and couldn't carve out the time to use it if we did.

Enter Big Thinking Day. A mini monthly retreat you give yourself to quiet the roar of daily demands and get the big thinking done.

Getting Ready

1. Set the time.

At the beginning of every month, set aside a minimum of four hours and find a spot where you can be alone. Any location can work: a chair in a shady spot of your back yard, a comfy couch by the fire, a library, a park, a friend's house, the beach. Put it on your calendar as blocked out time. Ask the cooperation of whomever you need to protect that time—only emergencies should be able to violate it. Be warned: this feels hard at first but gets easier as you see the benefits.

2. Gather the supplies.

Collect the provisions that will help create your idea of a nurturing day. Snacks, comfy clothes, music, notepads, and post-it notes. Select one of the instructional or inspirational books that have been sitting in your "I should read that" pile. If you are a creative person, include supplies for an artistic pursuit.

3. Set your intentions.

Get yourself in the habit of expecting good things from this time. If you are a person of faith, pray for both the protection of the time and the outcomes that are on the way. Feed your optimism for the value of this investment.

Big Thinking Day

1. Gather your positives.

Go back through the blessings/positives list from each day of the past month. Pick the ten that really make you smile and list them. It is a powerful thing to continually revisit our happinesses. Gratitude plants potent seeds of abundance.

2. Gather your "takeaways."

Read through your reflections from those same days, looking for "ah-ha" moments, realizations, and insights. Select the ten that feel most powerful, that point to larger issues, or that simply tell you something you didn't see before. List them. Patterns and trends will spring from these that you likely cannot see until you put them all together.

3. Tackle a larger issue.

Pick one issue—either one you've identified before or one that springs from the two steps above—and tackle it. It can be a professional issue like taking steps to land a new job or searching where you can acquire new skills. It might be a personal issue like planning a big vacation or finding out what program you'll use to shed those final twenty pounds. Maybe you're seeing an ongoing problem where you need to figure out what went wrong and lay out some action steps to fix it. Dream. Plan. Ponder how to make a big difference in your daily life. Maybe you need to find someone to guide or help you. There might be classes you should take or books you should read. Take a large issue and break it down into what steps you can take before the next Big Thinking Day and put those on your to-do list.

Get specific—what will you do next week? The week after? What do you want to have done a month from now?

4. Include time for creativity, self-care, and general de-stressing.

Do something nice for yourself that you never seem to have time to do. Bake, knit, visit a garden, take a bath, paint, listen to music—whatever feels like a gift to yourself.

5. Set a declaration.

Take everything that has bubbled to the surface during your Big Thinking Day and write out a declaration. Seriously. Read it—or better yet, say it out loud—every day for the next month. It may seem silly at first, but the power of this may astonish you. Think of it as a set of promises to yourself.

Some examples:

- I will make prospecting calls to generate five new clients.
- I will be thankful, knowing it brings forth abundance.
- I will look for the good in people that frustrate me.
- I will seek to understand rather than to judge.
- I will be more intentional in what I eat.
- I will drink eight glasses of water every day.

At the end of the year, you can look back over your twelve Big Thinking Days and see concrete evidence of how you have grown and changed over the year. It is powerful stuff, and the best source of fuel for ongoing improvements.

Daily Page

Date:_____

Inspirational Reading: _____

1) _____

2) _____

3) _____

1) _____ ☐

2) _____ ☐

3) _____ ☐

1) _____ ☐

2) _____ ☐

3) _____ ☐

1) _____ ☐

Daily Page

Date:_____

💡 **Inspirational Reading:** _____

1) _____

2) _____

3) _____

1) _____ ☐

2) _____ ☐

3) _____ ☐

1) _____ ☐

2) _____ ☐

3) _____ ☐

1) _____ ☐

Daily Page

Date:_____

Inspirational Reading: _____

1) _____

2) _____

3) _____

1) _____ ☐

2) _____ ☐

3) _____ ☐

1) _____ ☐

2) _____ ☐

3) _____ ☐

1) _____ ☐

Daily Page

Date:_____

Inspirational Reading: _____

1) _____

2) _____

3) _____

1) _____ ☐

2) _____ ☐

3) _____ ☐

1) _____ ☐

2) _____ ☐

3) _____ ☐

1) _____ ☐

Daily Page

Date:_____

Inspirational Reading: _____

1) _____

2) _____

3) _____

1) _____ ☐

2) _____ ☐

3) _____ ☐

1) _____ ☐

2) _____ ☐

3) _____ ☐

1) _____ ☐

Daily Page

Date:_____

🔖 **Inspirational Reading:** _____

1) _____

2) _____

3) _____

1) _____ ☐

2) _____ ☐

3) _____ ☐

1) _____ ☐

2) _____ ☐

3) _____ ☐

1) _____ ☐

Daily Page

Date:_____

Inspirational Reading: _____

1) _____

2) _____

3) _____

1) _____ ☐

2) _____ ☐

3) _____ ☐

1) _____ ☐

2) _____ ☐

3) _____ ☐

1) _____ ☐

Daily Page

Date:_____

Inspirational Reading: _____

1) _____

2) _____

3) _____

1) _____ ☐

2) _____ ☐

3) _____ ☐

1) _____ ☐

2) _____ ☐

3) _____ ☐

1) _____ ☐

Daily Page

Date:_____

Inspirational Reading: _____

1) _____

2) _____

3) _____

1) _____ ☐

2) _____ ☐

3) _____ ☐

1) _____ ☐

2) _____ ☐

3) _____ ☐

1) _____ ☐

Daily Page

Date:_____

Inspirational Reading: _____

1) _____

2) _____

3) _____

1) _____ ☐

2) _____ ☐

3) _____ ☐

1) _____ ☐

2) _____ ☐

3) _____ ☐

1) _____ ☐

Date_____

Daily Page

Date:_____

Inspirational Reading: _____

1) _____

2) _____

3) _____

1) _____ ☐

2) _____ ☐

3) _____ ☐

1) _____ ☐

2) _____ ☐

3) _____ ☐

1) _____ ☐

Daily Page

Date:_____

Inspirational Reading: _____

1) _____

2) _____

3) _____

1) _____ ☐

2) _____ ☐

3) _____ ☐

1) _____ ☐

2) _____ ☐

3) _____ ☐

1) _____ ☐

Date_____

Daily Page

Date:_____

Inspirational Reading: _____

1) _____

2) _____

3) _____

1) _____ ☐

2) _____ ☐

3) _____ ☐

1) _____ ☐

2) _____ ☐

3) _____ ☐

1) _____ ☐

Daily Page

Date:_____

Inspirational Reading: _____

1) _____

2) _____

3) _____

1) _____ ☐

2) _____ ☐

3) _____ ☐

1) _____ ☐

2) _____ ☐

3) _____ ☐

1) _____ ☐

Daily Page

Date:_____

Inspirational Reading: _____

1) _____

2) _____

3) _____

1) _____ ☐

2) _____ ☐

3) _____ ☐

1) _____ ☐

2) _____ ☐

3) _____ ☐

1) _____ ☐

Daily Page

Date:_____

Inspirational Reading: _____

1) _____

2) _____

3) _____

1) _____ ☐

2) _____ ☐

3) _____ ☐

1) _____ ☐

2) _____ ☐

3) _____ ☐

1) _____ ☐

Daily Page

Date:_____

Inspirational Reading: _____

1) _____

2) _____

3) _____

1) _____ ☐

2) _____ ☐

3) _____ ☐

1) _____ ☐

2) _____ ☐

3) _____ ☐

1) _____ ☐

Daily Page

Date:_____

💡 **Inspirational Reading:** _____

1) _____

2) _____

3) _____

1) _____ ☐

2) _____ ☐

3) _____ ☐

1) _____ ☐

2) _____ ☐

3) _____ ☐

1) _____ ☐

Daily Page

Date:_____

Inspirational Reading: _____

1) _____

2) _____

3) _____

1) _____ ☐

2) _____ ☐

3) _____ ☐

1) _____ ☐

2) _____ ☐

3) _____ ☐

1) _____ ☐

Daily Page

Date:_____

Inspirational Reading: _____

1) _____

2) _____

3) _____

1) _____ ☐

2) _____ ☐

3) _____ ☐

1) _____ ☐

2) _____ ☐

3) _____ ☐

1) _____ ☐

Daily Page

Date:_____

Inspirational Reading: _____

1) _____

2) _____

3) _____

1) _____ ☐

2) _____ ☐

3) _____ ☐

1) _____ ☐

2) _____ ☐

3) _____ ☐

1) _____ ☐

Daily Page

Date:_____

Inspirational Reading: _____

1) _____

2) _____

3) _____

1) _____ ☐

2) _____ ☐

3) _____ ☐

1) _____ ☐

2) _____ ☐

3) _____ ☐

1) _____ ☐

Daily Page

Date:_____

Inspirational Reading: _____

1) _____

2) _____

3) _____

1) _____ ☐

2) _____ ☐

3) _____ ☐

1) _____ ☐

2) _____ ☐

3) _____ ☐

1) _____ ☐

Date_____

Daily Page

Date:_____

Inspirational Reading: _____

1) _____

2) _____

3) _____

1) _____ ☐

2) _____ ☐

3) _____ ☐

1) _____ ☐

2) _____ ☐

3) _____ ☐

1) _____ ☐

Daily Page

Date:_____

💡 **Inspirational Reading:** _____

1) _____

2) _____

3) _____

1) _____ ☐

2) _____ ☐

3) _____ ☐

1) _____ ☐

2) _____ ☐

3) _____ ☐

1) _____ ☐

Daily Page

Date:_____

Inspirational Reading: _____

1) _____

2) _____

3) _____

1) _____ ☐

2) _____ ☐

3) _____ ☐

1) _____ ☐

2) _____ ☐

3) _____ ☐

1) _____ ☐

Daily Page

Date:_____

💡 **Inspirational Reading:** _____

1) _____

2) _____

3) _____

1) _____ ☐

2) _____ ☐

3) _____ ☐

1) _____ ☐

2) _____ ☐

3) _____ ☐

1) _____ ☐

Daily Page

Date:_____

Inspirational Reading: _____

1) _____

2) _____

3) _____

1) _____ ☐

2) _____ ☐

3) _____ ☐

1) _____ ☐

2) _____ ☐

3) _____ ☐

1) _____ ☐

Daily Page

Date:_____

Inspirational Reading: _____

1) _____

2) _____

3) _____

1) _____ ☐

2) _____ ☐

3) _____ ☐

1) _____ ☐

2) _____ ☐

3) _____ ☐

1) _____ ☐

Daily Page

Date:_____

Inspirational Reading: _____

1) _____

2) _____

3) _____

1) _____ ☐

2) _____ ☐

3) _____ ☐

1) _____ ☐

2) _____ ☐

3) _____ ☐

1) _____ ☐

Daily Page

Date:_____

Inspirational Reading: _____

1) _____

2) _____

3) _____

1) _____ ☐

2) _____ ☐

3) _____ ☐

1) _____ ☐

2) _____ ☐

3) _____ ☐

1) _____ ☐

Big Thinking Day

Month_____

Top 10 positives from this past month:

1)_____

2)_____

3)_____

4)_____

5)_____

6)_____

7)_____

8)_____

9)_____

10)_____

op 10 takeaways from this past month:

1) _____

2) _____

3) _____

4) _____

5) _____

6) _____

7) _____

8) _____

9) _____

10) _____

Self-care activity for today:

_____

_____

Larger issue to tackle:

_____

_____

Reflections/plans/ideas:

_____

_____

_____

_____

_____

_____

_____

_____

_____

_____

_____

_____

Goals for the coming month:

1)_____

2)_____

3)_____

4)_____

5)_____

Declaration for the coming month:

_____

_____

_____

_____

_____

_____

_____

_____

_____

_____

Month 2

Daily Page

Date:_____

Inspirational Reading: _____

1) _____

2) _____

3) _____

1) _____ ☐

2) _____ ☐

3) _____ ☐

1) _____ ☐

2) _____ ☐

3) _____ ☐

1) _____ ☐

Daily Page

Date:_____

Inspirational Reading: _____

1) _____

2) _____

3) _____

1) _____ ☐

2) _____ ☐

3) _____ ☐

1) _____ ☐

2) _____ ☐

3) _____ ☐

1) _____ ☐

Daily Page

Date:_____

Inspirational Reading: _____

1) _____

2) _____

3) _____

1) _____ ☐

2) _____ ☐

3) _____ ☐

1) _____ ☐

2) _____ ☐

3) _____ ☐

1) _____ ☐

Date_____

Daily Page

Date:_____

💡 **Inspirational Reading:** _____

1) _____

2) _____

3) _____

1) _____ ☐

2) _____ ☐

3) _____ ☐

1) _____ ☐

2) _____ ☐

3) _____ ☐

1) _____ ☐

Daily Page

Date:_____

Inspirational Reading: _____

1) _____

2) _____

3) _____

1) _____ ☐

2) _____ ☐

3) _____ ☐

1) _____ ☐

2) _____ ☐

3) _____ ☐

1) _____ ☐

Daily Page

Date:_____

Inspirational Reading: _____

1) _____

2) _____

3) _____

1) _____ ☐

2) _____ ☐

3) _____ ☐

1) _____ ☐

2) _____ ☐

3) _____ ☐

1) _____ ☐

Date_____

Daily Page

Date:_____

Inspirational Reading: _____

1) _____

2) _____

3) _____

1) _____ ☐

2) _____ ☐

3) _____ ☐

1) _____ ☐

2) _____ ☐

3) _____ ☐

1) _____ ☐

Daily Page

Date:_____

🔦 **Inspirational Reading:** _____

1) _____

2) _____

3) _____

1) _____ ☐

2) _____ ☐

3) _____ ☐

1) _____ ☐

2) _____ ☐

3) _____ ☐

1) _____ ☐

Date_____

Daily Page

Date:_____

Inspirational Reading: _____

1) _____

2) _____

3) _____

1) _____ ☐

2) _____ ☐

3) _____ ☐

1) _____ ☐

2) _____ ☐

3) _____ ☐

1) _____ ☐

Date_____

Daily Page

Date:_____

Inspirational Reading: _____

1) _____

2) _____

3) _____

1) _____ ☐

2) _____ ☐

3) _____ ☐

1) _____ ☐

2) _____ ☐

3) _____ ☐

1) _____ ☐

Daily Page

Date:_____

Inspirational Reading: _____

1) _____

2) _____

3) _____

1) _____ ☐

2) _____ ☐

3) _____ ☐

1) _____ ☐

2) _____ ☐

3) _____ ☐

1) _____ ☐

Daily Page

Date:_____

🔆 **Inspirational Reading:** _____

1) _____

2) _____

3) _____

1) _____ ☐

2) _____ ☐

3) _____ ☐

1) _____ ☐

2) _____ ☐

3) _____ ☐

1) _____ ☐

Daily Page

Date:_____

Inspirational Reading: _____

1) _____

2) _____

3) _____

1) _____ ☐

2) _____ ☐

3) _____ ☐

1) _____ ☐

2) _____ ☐

3) _____ ☐

1) _____ ☐

Date_____

Daily Page

Date:_____

Inspirational Reading: _____

1) _____

2) _____

3) _____

1) _____ ☐

2) _____ ☐

3) _____ ☐

1) _____ ☐

2) _____ ☐

3) _____ ☐

1) _____ ☐

Date_____

Daily Page

Date:_____

Inspirational Reading: _____

1) _____

2) _____

3) _____

1) _____ ☐

2) _____ ☐

3) _____ ☐

1) _____ ☐

2) _____ ☐

3) _____ ☐

1) _____ ☐

Daily Page

Date:_____

Inspirational Reading: _____

1) _____

2) _____

3) _____

1) _____ ☐

2) _____ ☐

3) _____ ☐

1) _____ ☐

2) _____ ☐

3) _____ ☐

1) _____ ☐

Date_____

Daily Page

Date:_____

Inspirational Reading: _____

1) _____

2) _____

3) _____

1) _____ ☐

2) _____ ☐

3) _____ ☐

1) _____ ☐

2) _____ ☐

3) _____ ☐

1) _____ ☐

Daily Page

Date:_____

Inspirational Reading: _____

1) _____

2) _____

3) _____

1) _____ ☐

2) _____ ☐

3) _____ ☐

1) _____ ☐

2) _____ ☐

3) _____ ☐

1) _____ ☐

Date_____

Daily Page

Date:_____

Inspirational Reading: _____

1) _____

2) _____

3) _____

1) _____ ☐

2) _____ ☐

3) _____ ☐

1) _____ ☐

2) _____ ☐

3) _____ ☐

1) _____ ☐

Daily Page

Date:_____

🔖 **Inspirational Reading:** _____

1) _____

2) _____

3) _____

1) _____ ☐

2) _____ ☐

3) _____ ☐

1) _____ ☐

2) _____ ☐

3) _____ ☐

1) _____ ☐

Date_____

Daily Page

Date:_____

💡 **Inspirational Reading:** _____

🌈

1) _____

2) _____

3) _____

🪜

1) _____ ☐

2) _____ ☐

3) _____ ☐

🚫

1) _____ ☐

2) _____ ☐

3) _____ ☐

⭐

1) _____ ☐

Daily Page

Date:_____

Inspirational Reading: _____

1) _____

2) _____

3) _____

1) _____ ☐

2) _____ ☐

3) _____ ☐

1) _____ ☐

2) _____ ☐

3) _____ ☐

1) _____ ☐

Daily Page

Date:_____

🪔 **Inspirational Reading:** _____

🌈

1) _____

2) _____

3) _____

🪜

1) _____ ☐

2) _____ ☐

3) _____ ☐

🎙️

1) _____ ☐

2) _____ ☐

3) _____ ☐

⭐

1) _____ ☐

Date_____

Daily Page

Date:_____

🔖 **Inspirational Reading:** _____

🌈

1) _____

2) _____

3) _____

🪜

1) _____ ☐

2) _____ ☐

3) _____ ☐

🎤

1) _____ ☐

2) _____ ☐

3) _____ ☐

⭐

1) _____ ☐

Daily Page

Date:_____

Inspirational Reading: _____

1) _____

2) _____

3) _____

1) _____ ☐

2) _____ ☐

3) _____ ☐

1) _____ ☐

2) _____ ☐

3) _____ ☐

1) _____ ☐

Date_____

Daily Page

Date:_____

Inspirational Reading: _____

1) _____

2) _____

3) _____

1) _____ ☐

2) _____ ☐

3) _____ ☐

1) _____ ☐

2) _____ ☐

3) _____ ☐

1) _____ ☐

Daily Page

Date:_____

💡 **Inspirational Reading:** _____

🌈

1) _____

2) _____

3) _____

1) _____ ☐

2) _____ ☐

3) _____ ☐

1) _____ ☐

2) _____ ☐

3) _____ ☐

1) _____ ☐

Date_____

Daily Page

Date:_____

Inspirational Reading: _____

1) _____

2) _____

3) _____

1) _____ ☐

2) _____ ☐

3) _____ ☐

1) _____ ☐

2) _____ ☐

3) _____ ☐

1) _____ ☐

Daily Page

Date:_____

💡 **Inspirational Reading:** _____

1) _____

2) _____

3) _____

1) _____ ☐

2) _____ ☐

3) _____ ☐

1) _____ ☐

2) _____ ☐

3) _____ ☐

1) _____ ☐

Daily Page

Date:_____

Inspirational Reading: _____

1) _____

2) _____

3) _____

1) _____ ☐

2) _____ ☐

3) _____ ☐

1) _____ ☐

2) _____ ☐

3) _____ ☐

1) _____ ☐

Date_____

Daily Page

Date:_____

Inspirational Reading: _____

1) _____

2) _____

3) _____

1) _____ ☐

2) _____ ☐

3) _____ ☐

1) _____ ☐

2) _____ ☐

3) _____ ☐

1) _____ ☐

Date_____

Big Thinking Day

Month_____

Top 10 positives from this past month:

1)_____

2)_____

3)_____

4)_____

5)_____

6)_____

7)_____

8)_____

9)_____

10)_____

Top 10 takeaways from this past month:

1)_____

2)_____

3)_____

4)_____

5)_____

6)_____

7)_____

8)_____

9)_____

10)_____

Self-care activity for today:

_____

_____

Larger issue to tackle:

_____

_____

Reflections/plans/ideas:

_____

_____

_____

_____

_____

_____

_____

_____

_____

_____

_____

Goals for the coming month:

1)_____

2)_____

3)_____

4)_____

5)_____

Declaration for the coming month:

Month 3

Daily Page

Date:_____

Inspirational Reading: _____

1) _____

2) _____

3) _____

1) _____ ☐

2) _____ ☐

3) _____ ☐

1) _____ ☐

2) _____ ☐

3) _____ ☐

1) _____ ☐

Date_____

Daily Page

Date:_____

Inspirational Reading: _____

1) _____

2) _____

3) _____

1) _____ ☐

2) _____ ☐

3) _____ ☐

1) _____ ☐

2) _____ ☐

3) _____ ☐

1) _____ ☐

Daily Page

Date:_____

Inspirational Reading: _____

1) _____

2) _____

3) _____

1) _____ ☐

2) _____ ☐

3) _____ ☐

1) _____ ☐

2) _____ ☐

3) _____ ☐

1) _____ ☐

Date_____

Daily Page

Date:_____

Inspirational Reading: _____

1) _____

2) _____

3) _____

1) _____ ☐

2) _____ ☐

3) _____ ☐

1) _____ ☐

2) _____ ☐

3) _____ ☐

1) _____ ☐

Date_____

Daily Page

Date:_____

Inspirational Reading: _____

1) _____

2) _____

3) _____

1) _____ ☐

2) _____ ☐

3) _____ ☐

1) _____ ☐

2) _____ ☐

3) _____ ☐

1) _____ ☐

Date_____

Daily Page

Date:_____

🔆 **Inspirational Reading:** _____

🌈

1) _____

2) _____

3) _____

🪜

1) _____ ☐

2) _____ ☐

3) _____ ☐

🎤

1) _____ ☐

2) _____ ☐

3) _____ ☐

⭐

1) _____ ☐

Date_____

Daily Page

Date:_____

Inspirational Reading: _____

1) _____

2) _____

3) _____

1) _____ ☐

2) _____ ☐

3) _____ ☐

1) _____ ☐

2) _____ ☐

3) _____ ☐

1) _____ ☐

Date_____

Daily Page

Date:_____

Inspirational Reading: _____

1) _____

2) _____

3) _____

1) _____ ☐

2) _____ ☐

3) _____ ☐

1) _____ ☐

2) _____ ☐

3) _____ ☐

1) _____ ☐

Date_____

Daily Page

Date:_____

Inspirational Reading: _____

1) _____

2) _____

3) _____

1) _____ ☐

2) _____ ☐

3) _____ ☐

1) _____ ☐

2) _____ ☐

3) _____ ☐

1) _____ ☐

Date_____

Daily Page

Date:_____

🔆 **Inspirational Reading:** _____

🌈

1) _____

2) _____

3) _____

1) _____ ☐

2) _____ ☐

3) _____ ☐

1) _____ ☐

2) _____ ☐

3) _____ ☐

1) _____ ☐

Date_____

Daily Page

Date:_____

Inspirational Reading: _____

1) _____

2) _____

3) _____

1) _____ ☐

2) _____ ☐

3) _____ ☐

1) _____ ☐

2) _____ ☐

3) _____ ☐

1) _____ ☐

Date_____

Daily Page

Date:_____

💡 **Inspirational Reading:** _____

1) _____

2) _____

3) _____

1) _____ ☐

2) _____ ☐

3) _____ ☐

1) _____ ☐

2) _____ ☐

3) _____ ☐

1) _____ ☐

Date_____

Daily Page

Date:_____

Inspirational Reading: _____

1) _____

2) _____

3) _____

1) _____ ☐

2) _____ ☐

3) _____ ☐

1) _____ ☐

2) _____ ☐

3) _____ ☐

1) _____ ☐

Date_____

Daily Page

Date:_____

Inspirational Reading: _____

1) _____

2) _____

3) _____

1) _____ ☐

2) _____ ☐

3) _____ ☐

1) _____ ☐

2) _____ ☐

3) _____ ☐

1) _____ ☐

Date_____

Daily Page

Date:_____

Inspirational Reading: _____

1) _____

2) _____

3) _____

1) _____ ☐

2) _____ ☐

3) _____ ☐

1) _____ ☐

2) _____ ☐

3) _____ ☐

1) _____ ☐

Date_____

Daily Page

Date:_____

Inspirational Reading: _____

1) _____

2) _____

3) _____

1) _____ ☐

2) _____ ☐

3) _____ ☐

1) _____ ☐

2) _____ ☐

3) _____ ☐

1) _____ ☐

Date_____

Daily Page

Date:_____

🔖 **Inspirational Reading:** _____

1) _____

2) _____

3) _____

1) _____ ☐

2) _____ ☐

3) _____ ☐

1) _____ ☐

2) _____ ☐

3) _____ ☐

1) _____ ☐

Date_____

Daily Page

Date:_____

Inspirational Reading: _____

1) _____

2) _____

3) _____

1) _____ ☐

2) _____ ☐

3) _____ ☐

1) _____ ☐

2) _____ ☐

3) _____ ☐

1) _____ ☐

Date_____

Daily Page

Date:_____

🔆 **Inspirational Reading:** _____

1) _____

2) _____

3) _____

1) _____ ☐

2) _____ ☐

3) _____ ☐

1) _____ ☐

2) _____ ☐

3) _____ ☐

1) _____ ☐

Date_____

Daily Page

Date:_____

Inspirational Reading: _____

1) _____

2) _____

3) _____

1) _____ ☐

2) _____ ☐

3) _____ ☐

1) _____ ☐

2) _____ ☐

3) _____ ☐

1) _____ ☐

Date_____

Daily Page

Date:_____

Inspirational Reading: _____

1) _____

2) _____

3) _____

1) _____ ☐

2) _____ ☐

3) _____ ☐

1) _____ ☐

2) _____ ☐

3) _____ ☐

1) _____ ☐

Date_____

Daily Page

Date:_____

Inspirational Reading: _____

1) _____

2) _____

3) _____

1) _____ ☐

2) _____ ☐

3) _____ ☐

1) _____ ☐

2) _____ ☐

3) _____ ☐

1) _____ ☐

Date_____

Daily Page

Date:_____

Inspirational Reading: _____

1) _____

2) _____

3) _____

1) _____ ☐

2) _____ ☐

3) _____ ☐

1) _____ ☐

2) _____ ☐

3) _____ ☐

1) _____ ☐

Date_____

Daily Page

Date:_____

Inspirational Reading: _____

1) _____

2) _____

3) _____

1) _____ ☐

2) _____ ☐

3) _____ ☐

1) _____ ☐

2) _____ ☐

3) _____ ☐

1) _____ ☐

Date_____

Daily Page

Date:_____

🔖 **Inspirational Reading:** _____

1) _____

2) _____

3) _____

1) _____ ☐

2) _____ ☐

3) _____ ☐

1) _____ ☐

2) _____ ☐

3) _____ ☐

1) _____ ☐

Date_____

Daily Page

Date:_____

Inspirational Reading: _____

1) _____

2) _____

3) _____

1) _____ ☐

2) _____ ☐

3) _____ ☐

1) _____ ☐

2) _____ ☐

3) _____ ☐

1) _____ ☐

Date_____

Daily Page

Date:_____

💡 **Inspirational Reading:** _____

1) _____

2) _____

3) _____

1) _____ ☐

2) _____ ☐

3) _____ ☐

1) _____ ☐

2) _____ ☐

3) _____ ☐

1) _____ ☐

Date_____

Daily Page

Date:_____

Inspirational Reading: _____

1) _____

2) _____

3) _____

1) _____ ☐

2) _____ ☐

3) _____ ☐

1) _____ ☐

2) _____ ☐

3) _____ ☐

1) _____ ☐

Date_____

Daily Page

Date:_____

Inspirational Reading: _____

1) _____

2) _____

3) _____

1) _____ ☐

2) _____ ☐

3) _____ ☐

1) _____ ☐

2) _____ ☐

3) _____ ☐

1) _____ ☐

Date_____

Daily Page

Date:_____

Inspirational Reading: _____

1) _____

2) _____

3) _____

1) _____ ☐

2) _____ ☐

3) _____ ☐

1) _____ ☐

2) _____ ☐

3) _____ ☐

1) _____ ☐

Date_____

Daily Page

Date:_____

Inspirational Reading: _____

1) _____

2) _____

3) _____

1) _____ ☐

2) _____ ☐

3) _____ ☐

1) _____ ☐

2) _____ ☐

3) _____ ☐

1) _____ ☐

Date_____

Big Thinking Day

Month_____

Top 10 positives from this past month:

1)_____

2)_____

3)_____

4)_____

5)_____

6)_____

7)_____

8)_____

9)_____

10)_____

Top 10 takeaways from this past month:

1)_____

2)_____

3)_____

4)_____

5)_____

6)_____

7)_____

8)_____

9)_____

10)_____

Self-care activity for today:

_____

_____

Larger issue to tackle:

_____

_____

Reflections/plans/ideas:

_____

_____

_____

_____

_____

_____

_____

_____

_____

_____

_____

Goals for the coming month:

1)_____

2)_____

3)_____

4)_____

5)_____

Declaration for the coming month:

Conclusion

I hope this journal has launched you on your way to a practice that is rewarding, insightful, and effective. As I said earlier, I believe this daily and monthly practice to be the single most influential element in my personal and professional success as a writer, a speaker, a parent, a spouse, a person of faith, and a member of my community.

I love to share these momentum ideas and tactics with audiences. You can find out more about my speaking at: *Alliepleiter.com*

Or you can reach me at allie@alliepleiter.com. I would welcome the opportunity to hear from you about how this book helped you.

If you'd like to go deeper on how this practice supports a creative career—especially for writers—I encourage you to read:
How to WRITE When Everything Goes WRONG
A Practical Guide to Writing Through Tough Times

If you are interested in my productivity book for writers, check out
The Chunky Method Handbook
Your Step by Step Plan to WRITE THAT BOOK
Even When Life Gets in the Way

Until then, accept my best wishes and fervent prayers for a momentum-filled, productive life.

Regards,

Allie

Made in USA - North Chelmsford, MA
1283007_9781735727301
10.12.2021 1329